John huehnergarth

PUZZLES, STUNTS, BRAIN TEASERS and TRICKS from "TELL ME WHY"

By ARKADY LEOKUM

Illustrated by JOHN HUEHNERGARTH

Library of Congress Catalog Card Number: 75-86724

Text Copyright © 1969, by Arkady Leokum
Illustrations © 1969, by Grosset & Dunlap, Inc.
Published simultaneously in Canada.   Printed in the United States of America.

GROSSET & DUNLAP · Publishers · NEW YORK

Contents

THREE BREATHTAKING TRICKS

Hang two apples by means of string from a towel rack or any similar support. The apples themselves should hang about one inch apart.

If you or a friend will now blow between them—as hard as possible—you will discover that the force of breath alone won't blow them apart. Instead, it will cause the apples to bump together!

Take a small piece of paper, about one inch square, and roll it into a small tight ball.

Now lay a soda bottle on its side—it is empty, of course—and push the small paper pellet into the neck of the bottle, about an inch from the opening. (Use your finger, or a pencil.)

What do you suppose would happen if you blew into the bottle? Do you think the tiny paper ball would be blown into it?

Try it. When you blow into the bottle, the ball will come flying out!

Your breath can lift a heavy book! Here's how to do it:

Put a large dictionary or heavy book directly on top of a hot-water bottle. When you hold the mouth of the bag tightly against your mouth and blow hard, the book will be raised quite easily.

THREE POSERS

Play detective and see if you can solve this puzzle:

A man who was served a cup of coffee in a restaurant called the waiter back to the table. Pointing to the cup, he said, "There seems to be a fly in my coffee. Please take this cup away and bring me a fresh cup of coffee."

The waiter promptly apologized, picked up the cup of coffee and took it away. He returned with a cup of coffee that had no fly in it. But when the customer tasted the coffee, he declared, "This is the same cup of coffee I had before!"

How did he know?

A medieval magician, carrying a bottle of liquid, approached the throne of his king.

"Sire," the magician said to the monarch, "I have here a most magic liquid. Such is its power that it will dissolve anything it touches."

"Anything?" asked the king.

"Anything!" replied the magician.

But the king knew that the magician was mistaken. How did he know?

A cannon ball is dropped from the top of a tower 250 feet high. At the same instant, another cannon ball of the same size and weight is fired horizontally (straight out) from a cannon.

Which cannon ball will reach the ground first?

Answers at back of the book.

SCRAMBLED NAMES

To look at these names, you might never think that they were three great men who were leaders of the fight for American independence.

Of course, the letters have been rearranged in each case. What you will have to do is to bring the letters into their original order to find out who these outstanding men were.

FNIRKNAL
FRONEFESJ
GNOTWINHAS

SONBIL
VENAGE
SLURSEBS

These are the names of three cities in Europe. No, not the way they are shown here —the letters have been rearranged in each case.

To find out what the cities are, bring the letters into their original order.

Three important professions are indicated by the names shown here, though the letters have been rearranged in each case.

To find out what the professions are, bring the letters into their original order.

CRATEHE
WAYREL
ISTENCTIS

HOW MANY?

In all of these puzzles, use the letters given
in any order, but only as often as they appear
in the boxes.

*Fox, Frog, Toad,
Dog, Cat*

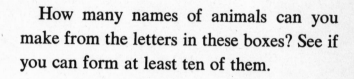

A	X	R	O
F	I	G	T
D	C	H	E

How many names of animals can you
make from the letters in these boxes? See if
you can form at least ten of them.

How many words about parts of the human body can you make from the letters in
these boxes? See if you can form at least nine
of them.

E	I	M
C	D	N
P	R	H
L	K	A

The letters in these boxes will also make
words about parts of the human body. See
if you can form at least ten of them.

E	I	T	C
N	S	A	O
F	P	H	M
O	R	L	B

10

Answers at back of the book.

*Ear, Nose, Lips, Arm,
Foot, Toes, Nail, Palms,
Hair*

CHANGE THE WORD

In these three puzzles, see if you can change the first word to the last one by changing only one letter in the word with each move. For example, you could change BOAT into CASH as follows: (BOAT, COAT, COST, CAST, CASH.) Use the boxes, writing in the words from top to bottom.

Answers for these puzzles will be found on page 44.

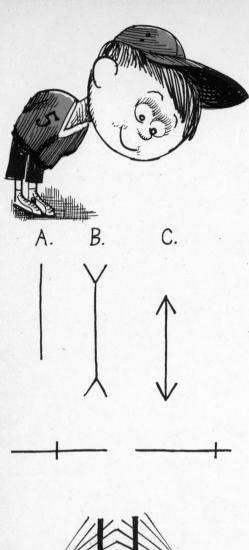

EYE FOOLERS

Here are some examples of how your own eyes can play tricks on you.

Which of the long lines shown in the figures marked A, B and C is the longest?

Most people would probably guess "B," but measurement will show that it is really "C."

Now ask someone to guess which of the two lines shown here is longer.

The truth is, they're equal in length. The right one seems longer because the vertical line pulls the eye beyond the end of the line.

Look at this illustration carefully. Are the two dark lines parallel (even with each other) or are they bent inward?

The lines are really not bent, but they appear to be that way because of the angles formed by the lighter lines.

Take two unsharpened pencils exactly the same size and set them in the form of a "T," as shown in the picture. Do this before you have a friend look at the formation. Then have him tell you which pencil is the longer one.

Most people will guess that the pencil forming the downstroke of the "T" is the longer one. Place the pencils side by side to show how wrong a guess can be.

CALENDAR CALCULATIONS

Don't throw away your old monthly calendar sheets—use them to show your friends this baffling trick:

Ask a friend to form an outline with pencil or crayon around nine dates on the calendar, the only restriction being that this is done in the form of a three-by-three square with all dates (numbers) included. There must be no blank spaces. You don't see what dates he chooses.

Now ask him to tell you the smallest of these numbers, whereupon, within a few short seconds, you are able to give him the sum (total) of all nine numbers! An amazing feat! It will take your friend a much longer time to add the numbers together himself and admit that the total you gave him is indeed correct.

To be able to do this, all you need do is add eight to the number your friend gives you (the smallest number) and multiply the result by nine.

Here's a way to use your hands to tell you how many days there are in each month. Hold up your fists, as shown in the picture. Start from the left and call the first knuckle January. The space before the next knuckle is February. The next knuckle is March,

All months that fall on knuckles have 31 days. All months that fall in the spaces between the knuckles have 30 days. In the case of February, of course, there are only 28 days, except during a leap year, when there are 29.

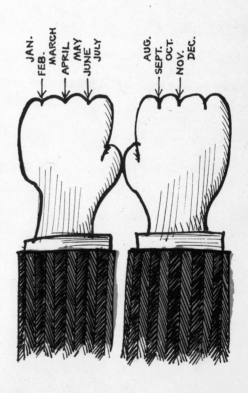

EGGS-TRAORDINARY
EGGS-HIBITIONS

This is a trick—really a demonstration of air pressure—that never ceases to amuse and amaze people.

Use a hard-boiled egg with its shell peeled off and a bottle whose opening is somewhat smaller than the narrow diameter of the egg. If you wish, you may want to challenge your friend to make the egg go through the neck of the bottle—without eating any of it, of course!

How can it be done? Simply drop a lighted match—or a small piece of paper that you have ignited with the match—into the bottle and immediately place the egg atop the bottle. The egg will be sucked right into the bottle!

The scientific explanation is that the burning of the match or paper uses up most of the oxygen within the bottle and creates a partial vacuum which forces the egg (the pressure of the outside air "pushes") through the narrower opening and into the bottle.

Place a fresh egg in a glass of water. After it sinks to the bottom, challenge your friends to bring the egg to the top of the glass without touching it. Here's how to do it:

Hold the glass under a water faucet and gradually turn on the water. As the flow increases, the egg will rise to the surface and stay there.

Challenge your friends to make an egg spin. They won't be able to do it. Then you show them that you apparently have some mysterious power, because you can make an egg spin without a bit of trouble.

The trick is that you give your friends an uncooked (raw) egg to spin. When you try, you use a hard-boiled egg. A fresh egg won't spin, but a hard-boiled one will!

It is said—though it is probably no more than a story having little or no basis in fact —that Christopher Columbus once amazed some people by being able to stand an egg on end.

You can do as well as Columbus in this particular instance. Just shake the egg that you will use—this is all done beforehand—so that the yolk will break. You may have to shake rather vigorously. Allow the broken yolk to settle for a few minutes.

When you are ready to "outdo" Columbus, just make sure that you have a table with a cloth on it and that you balance the egg carefully. You will find that you can do this without too much difficulty. (That will be YOUR discovery!)

It is also possible to do the previous egg trick another way—without breaking the yolk. The trick is to put a small amount of salt on the white tablecloth, to form a tiny mound. When you place the egg carefully into the salt, it will balance.

In this method, it is possible to brush away the salt (without, of course, calling attention to it) in the act of picking up the egg and handing it to someone, as you ask him to try to duplicate your feat. He will naturally not be able to do it.

TWENTY-FIVE DOTS

Copy this square of twenty-five dots and challenge a friend to connect twelve of these dots with straight lines to make a perfect cross that will have five dots inside it and eight dots outside.

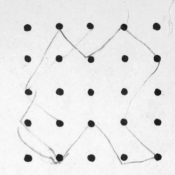

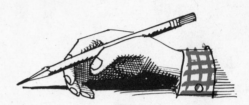

TEN DOTS

Can you draw four straight lines which will pass through every one of the dots shown here? You must not take your pencil off the paper!

Answers at back of the book.

FOUR DOTS

Copy the four dots exactly as shown. Then challenge someone to draw a square which has one of the four dots in each side.

16

AN INTERESTING YEAR

We had an interesting year a while back. Take that year and divide it by two. Turn the result upside-down and divide that by three. Take the number you get and divide it by two. Reverse the digits in the result and you get 13.

What is the year?

Answer may be found on page 44.

NUMBER, PLEASE

Give a friend two dice, turn your back, and have him toss them out on the table. Tell him to write down the number on one of the dice, multiply it by two, and add one to it. He then multiplies the result by five. Now he adds the number on the second dice and tells you the sum.

You now disclose the numbers uppermost on the dice.

How to do it: merely subtract five from the final number. Do it in your head. The first digit of that number is the same as the number on the first die; the second digit is the number on the second die.

17

MATCHING SQUARES

Take thirteen matches and arrange them to make four squares, as shown. The problem is to take away only one match and have exactly three squares left. (There must be no matches left over.)

The way to do it is shown on page 44.

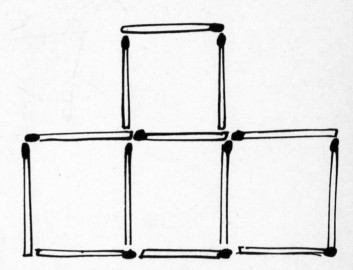

Form nine squares with 24 matches, as shown. The problem is to take away exactly eight matches—and leave only two squares.

The way to do it is shown on page 44.

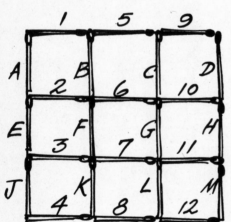

Break four wooden matches in the middle (not completely) and put them into a saucer to make a cross, as shown. Then announce that you can change the design into a star without touching it.

The way to do it is to drop a little water in the center area. The matches will spread apart to form a four-cornered star.

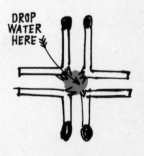

DROP WATER HERE

Crack four matches and form them into a cross, as shown. The problem is to make a square by moving one match.

The way to do it is shown on page 44.

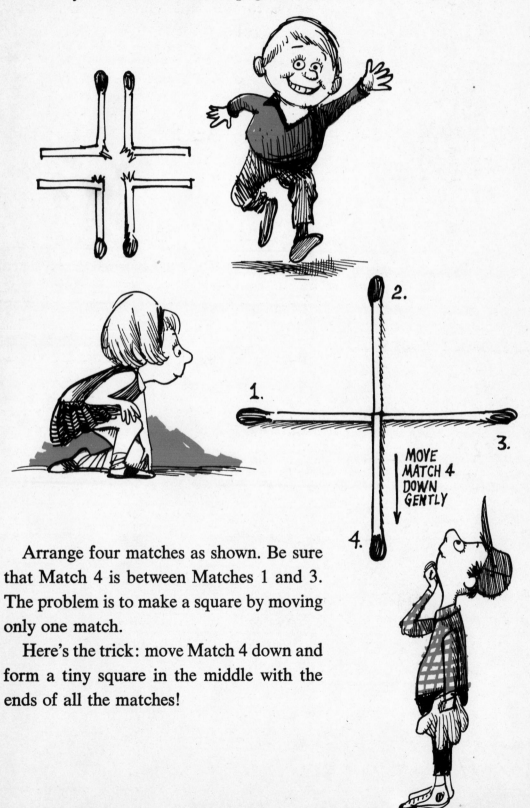

MOVE
MATCH 4
DOWN
GENTLY

Arrange four matches as shown. Be sure that Match 4 is between Matches 1 and 3. The problem is to make a square by moving only one match.

Here's the trick: move Match 4 down and form a tiny square in the middle with the ends of all the matches!

19

MATCHING NUMBERS

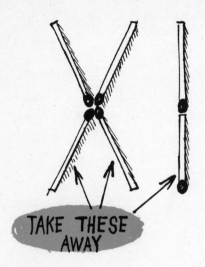

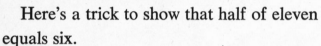

TAKE THESE AWAY

Here's a trick to show that half of eleven equals six.

Arrange six matches to form the Roman figure eleven (XI), as shown. Now take away the bottom three matches—or half of eleven—and the Roman number VI remains!

WHEN IN ROME, DO AS THE ROMANS DO!

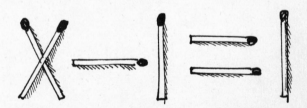

By arranging the matches as shown, an equation is formed in Roman numerals which reads ten minus one equals one. Obviously, this is not correct. How can you make it correct by merely changing the position of one match?

The answer is on page 44.

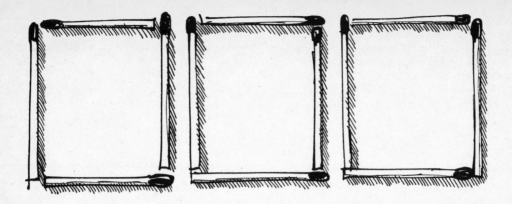

Arrange twelve matches to form three separate squares, as shown. Announce that you can take one match away and have one remain.

Impossible? No. Tricky? Yes. The answer will be found on page 44.

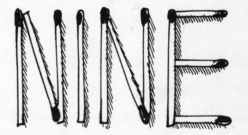

Hand your friend five matches. Then give him six more. Ask him to count them. When he says "Eleven," you say that he is mistaken. "Five matches plus six matches make nine!"

To prove it, take the eleven matches and arrange them to spell out the word NINE, as shown.

A variation of the last trick is to lay nine matches on the table and state that you will make ten out of the nine matches without breaking any.

Naturally, the way to do it is to form the word TEN with the matches, as shown.

DIVIDE BY SEVEN

This is a tricky problem, but it can be solved. The baseball players appear to be perplexed—and well they might be. They have been asked to arrange themselves so that the number on their uniforms form one number that can be divided evenly by seven.

Can you help them? Remember, we said it was tricky. The answer may be found on page 44.

PIG PEN

PIG PEN THIS WAY

PENS AND PIGS

This is another tricky problem, which is simply this: can you put nine pigs in four pens so that each of the four pens has an odd number of pigs?

Check your answer with that on page 44.

WORD MAGIC

Hand your friend a pencil and a pad or sheet of paper. Ask him to write a sentence on it, but not to show it to you.

You then say, "I will write the same as you on my paper"—and proceed to write something which will presumably match whatever he writes.

When the time comes for you to show what you've written, you do so. On your paper is written, "The same as you." That is exactly what you said you would do!

Can you think of an English word of four letters which reads the same upside-down as it does right side up, when printed in capital letters?

The word is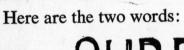

Can you think of an English word of four letters meaning "water" which becomes a word meaning "land" by the change of one letter?

Here are the two words:

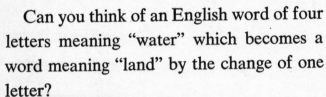

THE $700 MYSTERY

You may have to do a little thinking, and use pencil and paper, to solve this puzzle.

A man had $700. He divided it into quarters, half dollars and dollars so that there was an equal number of each. How many of each denomination did he divide it into?

Answers at back of the book.

THE DOLLAR MYSTERY

Have you ever examined a dollar bill closely? Do you remember what you saw on it?

See if you can answer this question: which way is Washington facing?

TWO MAD ADDERS

Here's a trick with numbers that will amaze your friends. Write the columns of figures as shown. Then put down "plus 2," as shown. Watch their surprise when they add the numbers and start arriving at a total.

1 2 3 4 5 6 7 8 9
9 8 7 6 5 4 3 2 1
1 2 3 4 5 6 7 8 9
9 8 7 6 5 4 3 2 1
PLUS 2
_____
2 2 2 2 2 2 2 2 2 2

15   25
  9   27
30   3
21   12
19   6

Copy the ten numbers shown here and challenge someone to draw a circle around as many numbers as he wishes to make them total exactly fifty.

The only numbers that will add up to fifty are . . . to be found on page 45.

A SECRET MESSAGE

Here's how to send a secret message. Dip a clean pen into vinegar and write the message on a sheet of heavy writing paper. Be sure to make a good heavy line as you write. This "ink" will soon dry and become invisible.

All your friend has to do to read the message is hold the paper an inch or two above a candle flame and move it back and forth slowly. The message will appear again!

THE MAGIC FLAME

Here's a way to light a candle without touching a flame to the wick of the candle.

First light a candle with a match. After it burns for a minute, blow it out. As soon as you blow it out, strike a match and hold it about an inch above the candlewick. The flame will actually jump down to the candle and light the wick.

The secret is to watch the curl of smoke that goes up from the candle after it has been put out. When the match meets this smoke, the flame shoots down to the candle.

THE UNDERWATER CANDLE

Here's how to make a candle burn below the surface of a glass of water.

Put a nail in the bottom of the candle so that the candle will float in a vertical position. Then light it. The melting wax will form a little well in which the wick will burn.

NAIL
IN
CANDLE

SHADOW OF A DIFFERENCE

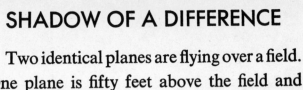

Two identical planes are flying over a field. One plane is fifty feet above the field and the other is five hundred feet above the field. What will be the difference in the size of their shadows?

The answer is: "no difference." Since the size of a shadow depends on the distance from the light source, and the sun is 93,-000,000 miles away, the slight difference of 450 feet between the two planes isn't enough to make a perceptible difference.

THROUGH THE TABLE

Get a lump of wrapped sugar, secretly unwrap it very carefully, and take out the sugar. Then close the ends of the paper so it looks as if the sugar is still in it.

Have the sugar in your lap beforehand.

To present, show the empty packet and place it a short distance away from you and the edge of the table. Then bring your hand down on it hard so it flattens the paper. The sugar is gone!

Now reach under the table and get the lump of sugar. Bring it forth and toss it on the table. The illusion has been that the sugar penetrated both its own wrapper and the solid table.

THE THREE R'S

Using the same two letters to fill in the
spaces on each line, can you complete these
three words?

See page 45 for the answer.

R _ _ _

_ R _ R _

_ _ _ R R

THE FOUR L'S

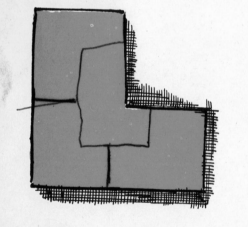

Draw the letter L, as shown, on a piece
of paper. The problem is to cut or form four
small L's within this area, all having the
same basic shape as the large one you see.

See page 45 for the answer.

CUTTING THE PIE

Next time Mother bakes a pie, try this on
her. Ask her what would be the most pieces
she can cut with four straight cuts.

Try to work it out, yourself.

Check the answer on page 45.

IT MAKES CENTS

Put four 1¢ pieces on the table and challenge someone to arrange them so that there are two straight lines with three cents in each line.

The trick is to lay out three of the 1¢ pieces in the form of a triangle, and then put the fourth cent on top of the others.

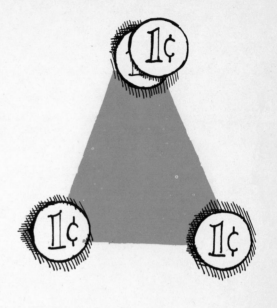

FIGURE IT OUT!

Can you figure out this number? It consists of two digits. If you multiply the digits and multiply the result by two, you get the actual number.

18
24 ? 32
14 . 46
98

Answers at back of the book.

A ONE-LINER

Look at this drawing carefully and then try to draw it with one continuous line. Do not cross any lines or go over any lines twice.

PICK UP THE ICE CUBE

Float an ice cube in a glass of water and challenge your friends to try to lift it out with a loop of string. They won't be able to do it.

Then you show them how easy it is. Wet the loop of string first, then lay it on the ice cube and sprinkle it with salt. After three minutes, lift the string and you will be able to lift out the ice cube.

A.   B.

PICK UP THE GLASS

Get a glass and a balloon. Challenge your friend to pick up the glass with the balloon—without touching the glass with his hands.

The way to do it—as you can demonstrate—is to hold the balloon inside the glass with the bottom part touching the bottom of the glass. Blow into the balloon, inflating it, close the top end—and you'll be able to lift the glass!

PICK UP THE DIME

Announce that you can pick up a dime from a table without touching the dime with any part of your body, and without using any metal, wood, or cardboard instrument.

The way to do it is to place the bottom opening of a drinking straw against the dime and suck up the air from the other end. You'll be able to pick up the dime.

THE VANISHING WATER

Cover a glass of water with a hat and say to your friend, "I bet I can drink all the water in that glass without touching the hat."

You really have to be tricky to do this. Take a pencil, put one end to your lips and the other end to the hat, and remark that it is a magic straw. Pretend that you are drinking the water, as you would an ice-cream soda. Then say, "All right — the water is gone."

When your friend lifts the hat to see if it's true, you simply pick up the glass and drink the water without ever touching the hat. (Your friend was the one who touched the hat when he lifted it up.)

THE WALKING DIME

Place a dime on a table that has a table-cloth. Then place a nickel on each side of the dime so that you can put a glass upside down on the two nickels, as shown in the picture.

Now challenge your friend to get the dime from under the glass without touching the glass, the dime, or the nickels.

The way to do it is to scratch the table-cloth with your fingernail as close to the glass as possible. Short fast scratches will soon cause the dime to "walk" out from under the glass.

HAVE A FEW FITS

Make this drawing on a large sheet of paper. Then cut the square into seven pieces along the lines shown. Mix up the pieces and challenge your friend to put them together so as to form a square. It won't be easy.

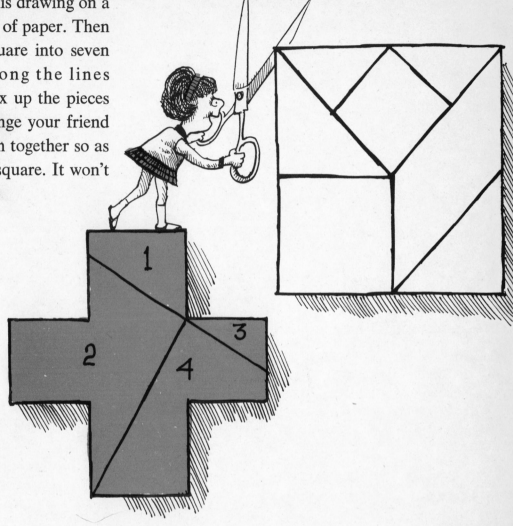

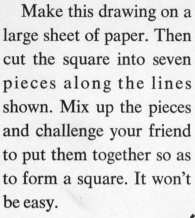

Copy this cross on a large sheet of paper. Cut it along the lines shown in the picture. Challenge your friend to put it together to make a cross. He'll find it harder than he thinks.

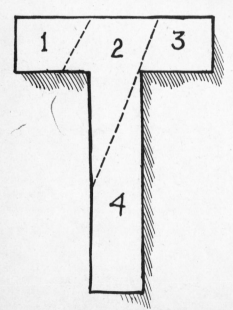

Copy the letter T, as shown, making it quite large. Draw the dotted lines, as shown, and cut it into four pieces along the dotted lines. Now challenge your friend to put the pieces together to make the letter T.

THE INVISIBLE THIMBLE

Here's a good joke to play on your friend. Tell him, "I bet I can put a thimble where everybody in the room can see it except you."

Then put the thimble on your friend's head.

THE IMPOSSIBLE FOLD

If you have a friend who thinks he's strong, give him a sheet of newspaper, two full pages. Challenge him to fold it eight times. He may think that there's nothing to it, but no matter how much he tries, he won't be able to fold it eight times.

The reason is that the paper would have 128 thicknesses on the eighth fold — and paper can't be folded that many times.

THE PROBLEM OF THE AGES

Try this on Dad and see if it does not keep him puzzled for a long time.

There are three brothers — Andy, Billy and Charlie. Andy is as old as Billy and Charlie put together. Last year, Billy was twice as old as Charlie. Two years from now, Andy will be twice as old as Charlie. What are the ages of the three brothers?

The answer may be found on page 45.

RING AND COIN

For this trick you need an ordinary finger ring and a quarter—or any coin which could not possibly pass through the ring.

Nevertheless, you announce with confidence that you can push the coin through the ring.

When someone challenges you to do it, just put your finger through the ring and push the quarter.

JUST GIVE THE WORD

The problem here is to rearrange the letters in the words NEW DOOR so they make one word.

The puzzle is also a trick, because you simply write what is shown.

one word

THREE FUNNY TRICKS

Here's a trick that's sure to fool your friend. Ask him to stand in front of you. Take a clothes brush and brush your own coat. At the same time, rub his coat lightly with the palm of your hand. When you ask him what you're doing, he's sure to say you're brushing HIS coat!

In this trick you announce, "I bet I can go out of the room on two legs and come back with six."

Someone is sure to want to see THAT! And what you do is simply pick up a chair in another room and bring it back with you!

Tell your friend, "I bet you can't take off your coat alone." As soon as he starts to take off his coat, though, you take your coat off, too!

PENCIL DRAWINGS

At a party—or any time—give your friend a pencil and paper, and then blindfold him. Now ask him to draw something—even the simplest object. Everyone will get a good laugh at the grotesque, fantastic and exaggerated sketches.

This can also be a test for your friends. Give them all a sheet of paper and a pencil and ask each one to draw a circle the size of a quarter, a line the length of a standard cigarette, and a rectangle the size of a postage stamp. When their drawings are compared with the actual things, it will be a surprise to everyone to discover the inaccuracies.

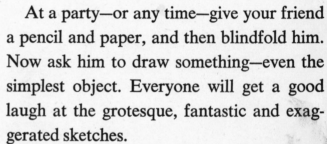

Draw an oblong box and challenge a friend to draw in the American flag from memory. You'll be surprised and amused to see how many mistakes he makes.

JOURNEY TO THE CENTER OF THE CIRCLE

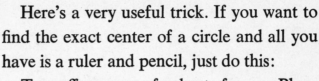

Here's a very useful trick. If you want to find the exact center of a circle and all you have is a ruler and pencil, just do this:

Tear off a corner of a sheet of paper. Place it on the circle, as shown in the picture. Where the sides of the paper touch the circle (A and B), make two marks. When you join them, you will have the diameter. And half that line will be the center of the circle.

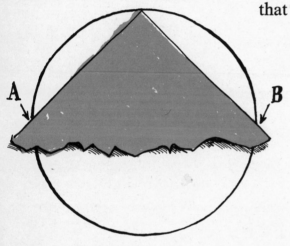

A STRAIGHT LINE

Tell your friends you can make a perfectly straight line across a table without using a ruler or any other object with a straight edge.

The trick is to take a long rubber band that has been cut, have the ends held for you, and then rub chalk along the band. Then ask your two friends to hold the rubber-band ends at opposite ends of the table. You take the center, stretch it up and let go. It will snap back and make a straight line on the table.

IT'S MAGNETISM!

Spill a little salt on a bare table. Now challenge someone to remove it—but without touching the table or the salt, and without blowing or fanning of any kind.

The trick is to rub an ordinary plastic comb on your sleeve several times and bring it near the salt. The salt will seem to jump to the comb.

You can make a playing card stick to a smooth wall without using paste, glue, tape or any adhesive, and without nails or tacks. It is done—preferably on a dry day—by shuffling your feet on the rug or carpet while holding the card in your hand. Then slam the card onto the wall. In cold weather, static electricity will cause the card to stick to the wall.

Tear a piece of paper into small scraps and place them on a table. Announce that you can "magnetize" a pencil so it will cause those papers to move. Rub the pencil on your sleeve, and as you bring it close to the paper, blow gently. The papers will move away as if the pencil is causing this movement. Be sure that no one sees you blowing.

NUMBER TRIANGLE

Form a triangle of nine circles, as shown, and try to solve this puzzle. You are to put numbers from 1 to 9 in the circles so that each side of the triangle adds up to 20.

Try it yourself and give the problem to your friends, too. The answer may be found on page 45.

CLIMBING WATER

This trick proves that water climbs. Fill a bottle with water to about three inches from the top. Wet a cloth handkerchief and squeeze it out gently. Put the handkerchief into the bottle and let one corner hang over the edge, as shown. In time the water will climb up the handkerchief and droplets of water will drop off the handkerchief.

MATCH THE ANSWER

Arrange sixteen matches as shown in the picture. Then say to your friends that when you take away four matches the remainder will show "what matches are made of."

Remove the four matches that are drawn black, and the remainder will spell "love."

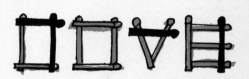

SEA WORDS

This is a word-forming puzzle. You form a five-letter word by choosing its first letter from the first vertical column, its second letter from the second vertical column, and so on, until you have a five-letter word.

The puzzle-problem is to form five words in this manner, all five words relating to the sea.

```
L H O H R
Y T E L E
W C N A M
O A A R N
S I C E T
```

Answers at back of the book.

```
- L U M -
- X T R -
- E B E -
- L O R -
- L F I -
- O M I -
- A B L -
```

LETTER FILL

In each of the letter combinations shown below you can form a word by adding a letter to the beginning and the end. The trick is to form words so that the first letters and the last letters will also form words when you read them from top to bottom.

THREE "HANDY" TRICKS

Tell your friend to put his hand flat on a table, with his middle finger under his hand, as shown in the picture. Now challenge him to lift his third finger without moving his middle finger. He won't be able to do it!

Here's a way to prove your friends don't know how to count!

Tell someone to cross his middle and index fingers and then close his eyes. Hold out your hand with two marbles in it. Ask him to touch the marbles with the tips of his crossed fingers and tell you how many there are. He's sure to say there are three or even four. His crossed fingers will fool him!

Ask your friend to stand with her back to you with her arms out. Now tell her to keep her arms straight and you take each of her wrists and pull her arms backward slowly. Make the backs of her hands touch.

When you do this, she simply won't believe that the backs of her hands were touching. It's a trick the senses play on us.

HUNTER IN A HURRY

A hunter ran into a panther, a puma, and a mountain lion. He fired only one bullet and killed them all! How is that possible?

See answer on page 45.

WHICH HAND?

Tell your friend to hold a penny in one hand and a nickel in the other. Now tell him to multiply the coin in one hand by 17. Now he does the same with the other coin. He adds the two results and tells you the sum. You immediately know which coin was in which hand.

The number your friend gives you has nothing to do with it. It's only a way of leading him astray—to fool him. You can point out the hand with the nickel because it took him longer to do the multiplication!

A DELICATE BALANCE

This is a trick to make your friends think you can balance a glass on the edge of a plate, as shown in the first picture.

Here's what you do. As you put the glass (which may contain liquid) on top of the plate, raise your thumb behind it to hold the glass in place, as shown in the second picture.

FRONT   BACK

SIX GLASSES

Arrange six glasses in a row, three of them filled with water or some other liquid, as shown.

The problem, you tell a friend, is to arrange the glasses so that they stand one filled, one empty, one filled, one empty, one filled, one empty. This must be done by moving or touching only one glass.

The way to do it is to take glass No. 4 and pour the water into glass No. 1, then replace glass No. 4.

THE FIREPROOF CUP

Did you know that you can hold a paper cup over a gas flame without having the paper cup catch fire?

The trick is to fill the cup with cold water. The heat will be conducted away by the cold water.

ANSWERS

Three Posers
(Page 8)

(1) The man knew it was the same cup of coffee because he had put sugar in the coffee before he found the fly in it.

(2) The king knew the magician was mistaken, because if the liquid dissolved everything it touched, it would dissolve the bottle, too.

(3) Both cannon balls will reach the ground at the same time. Gravity acts on each one in the same way, so each one will approach the ground at the same rate.

Scrambled Names
(Page 9)

(1) Franklin, Jefferson, Washington.

(2) Lisbon, Geneva, Brussels.

(3) Teacher, Lawyer, Scientist.

How Many?
(Page 10)

ANIMALS: Dog, hog, doe, goat, cat, toad, fox, frog, rat, tiger.

HUMAN BODY (1): Arm, ear, nail, chin, neck, hand, hair, ankle, lip.

HUMAN BODY (2): Ear, face, arm, toe, foot, nail, lip, nose, hair, rib, chest, bone, chin.

Change the Word
(Page 11)

LAST, PAST, PART, PERT, PERK
CLAN, PLAN, PLAY, PRAY, PREY
NEST, PEST, POST, PORT, PORK

Twenty-Five Dots
(Page 16)

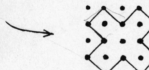

Ten Dots
(Page 16)

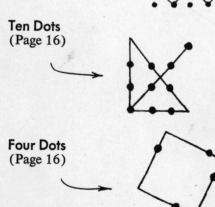

Four Dots
(Page 16)

An Interesting Year
(Page 17)

1962.

Matching Squares
(Pages 18-19)

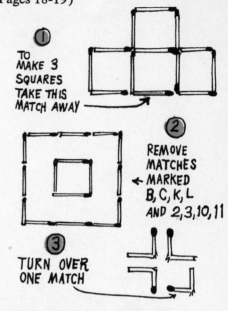

TO MAKE 3 SQUARES TAKE THIS MATCH AWAY →

② REMOVE MATCHES MARKED B, C, K, L AND 2, 3, 10, 11

③ TURN OVER ONE MATCH

Matching Numbers
(Pages 20-21)

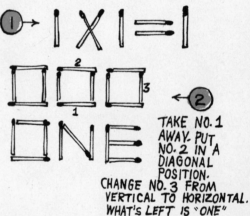

② TAKE NO. 1 AWAY. PUT NO. 2 IN A DIAGONAL POSITION. CHANGE NO. 3 FROM VERTICAL TO HORIZONTAL. WHAT'S LEFT IS "ONE"

Divide by Seven
(Page 22)

One of the players stands on his head, and the three players form the number 931.

Pens and Pigs
(Page 22)

First make one large pen, and then make three small pens inside it. Put three pigs in each of the small pens, and the large pen will have nine pigs!

The $700 Mystery
(Page 24)

Four hundred of each.

The Dollar Mystery
(Page 24)

George Washington faces to the right on a dollar bill.

Two Mad Adders
(Page 25)

The only numbers that add up to fifty are: 25, 6, and 19.

The Three R's
(Page 28)

Rat, art, tar.

The Four L's
(Page 28)

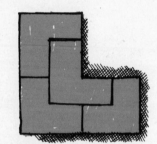

Cutting the Pie
(Page 28)

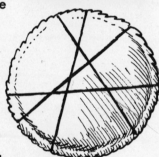

Figure it Out!
(Page 29)

36.

A One-Liner
(Page 29)

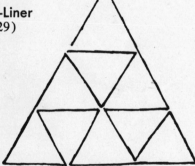

The Problem of the Ages
(Page 34)

Andy is 8, Billy is 5, and Charlie is 3.

Number Triangle
(Page 39)

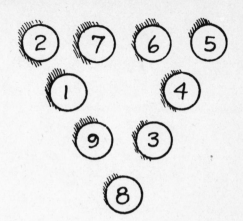

Sea Words
(Page 40)

Liner, yacht, whale, storm, ocean.

Letter Fill
(Page 40)

Plumb, extra, rebel, flora, elfin, comic, table.
The vertical words read "perfect balance."

Hunter in a Hurry
(Page 42)

They are all the same animal!

john huehnergarth